THIS BOOK BELONGS TO ....

Best~Loved Nursery Rhymes

Punch and Judy
Fought for a pie;
Punch gave Judy
A knock in the eye.

Says Punch to Judy,
'Will you have any more?'
Says Judy to Punch,
'My eye is too sore.'

SIX LITTLE MICE

Six little mice sat down to spin; Pussy passed by and she peeped in,
'What are you doing, my little men?' 'Weaving coats for gentlemen.'
'Shall I come in and cut off your threads?'
'No, no, Mistress Pussy, you'll bite off our heads.'
'Oh no, I'll not; I'll help you to spin.'
'That may be so, but you don't come in.'

COFFEE AND TEA

Molly, my sister, and I
  fell out,
And what do you think
  it was about?
She loved coffee and I
  loved tea,
And that was the reason
  we couldn't agree.

The Man in the moon
        came tumbling down,
To ask his way to Norwich.
He went by the south
        and burnt his mouth,
By eating cold plum-porridge.

There was an old woman
            tossed up in a basket,
Seventeen times as high as the
                        moon;
Where she was going
            I couldn't but ask her,
For in her hand she carried a
                        broom.
Old woman, old woman, old
                        woman,
                    quoth I,
Where are you going to up so
                        high!
To brush the cobwebs off the
                        sky!

May I go with you?
Yes, by-and-by.

One, two, three, four, five,
Once I caught a fish alive.
Six, seven, eight, nine, ten,
Then I let it go again.

Why did you let it go?
Because it bit my finger so.
Which finger did it bite?
This little finger on the right.

WINDY NIGHTS

Rumbling in the chimneys, rattling at the doors,
Round the roofs and round the roads the rude wind roars;
Raging through the darkness, raving through the trees,
Racing off again across the grey seas.

DEAR, DEAR!

Dear, dear! what can the matter be?
Two old women got up in an apple-tree;

One came down,
And the other stayed till Saturday.

There was a little boy and a little girl
    Lived in our alley;
Says the little boy to the little girl,
    "Shall I, oh, shall I?"
Says the little girl to the little boy,
    "What shall we do?"
Says the little boy to the little girl,
    "I will kiss you!"

Sing a song of sixpence,
A pocket full of rye:
Four and twenty blackbirds,
Baked in a pie.

When the pie was opened,
The birds began to sing;
Now wasn't that a dainty dish,
To set before the king?

COUNTING
HOUSE

The maid was in the garden,
Hanging out the clothes,
When down came a blackbird,
And pecked off her nose.

The king was in his counting-house,
Counting out his money;
The queen was in the parlour,
Eating bread and honey.

Jack Sprat could eat no fat,
His wife could eat no lean,
And so between them both, you see,
They licked the platter clean.

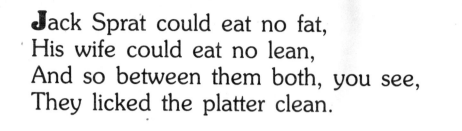

Mary, Mary, quite contrary,
How does your garden grow?
With silver bells and cockle shells
And pretty maids all in a row.

Yankee Doodle came to town,
Riding on a pony;
He stuck a feather in his cap
And called it macaroni.

There was a little man, and
he had a little gun,
And his bullets they were
made of lead, lead, lead.

He shot Johnny Sprig through
the middle of his wig,
And knocked it right
off his head, head, head.

There was an old woman who lived in a shoe,
She had so many children she didn't know what to do;
She gave them some broth without any bread;
Then whipped them all soundly and sent them to bed.

Pussy cat, pussy cat, where have you been?
I've been to London to look at the queen.
Pussy cat, pussy cat, what did you there?
I frightened a little mouse under a chair.

WASHING

What is all this washing about,
Every day, week in, week out?
From getting up till going to bed,
I'm tired of hearing the same thing said.
Whether I'm dirty or whether I'm not,
Whether the water is cold or hot,
Whether I like or whether I don't,
Whether I will or whether I won't, –
"Have you washed your hands and
    washed your face?"
I seem to live in the washing-place.

Whenever I go for a walk or ride,
As soon as I put my nose inside
The door again, there's someone there
With a sponge and soap, and a lot they
    care
If I have something better to do,
"Now wash your face and your fingers
    too."

Before a meal is ever begun,
And after ever a meal is done,
It's time to turn on the waterspout.

Please, what **is** all this washing about?"
John Drinkwater

Buttons, a farthing a pair,
Come, who will buy them of me?
They're round and sound and pretty,
And fit for the girls of the city.
Come, who will buy them of me,
Buttons, a farthing a pair?

Here's sulky Sue!
What shall we do?
Put her in the corner, till
she comes to.

Smiling girls, rosy boys,
Come and buy my little toys,
Monkeys made of gingerbread,
And sugar horses, painted red.

Ding, dong, bell,
Pussy's in the well.
Who put her in?
Little Johnny Green.
Who pulled her out?
Little Tommy Stout.

What a naughty boy was that,
To try to drown poor pussy cat,
Who never did him any harm,
And killed the mice in his father's barn.

Wee Willie Winkie
      runs through the town,
Upstairs and downstairs
      in his nightgown,
Knocking on the window,
      crying through the lock,
Are the children all in bed,
      it's past eight-o'clock?

Thirty days hath September,
April, June and November;
All the rest have thirty-one,
Excepting February alone,
And that has twenty-eight days clear
And twenty-nine in each leap year.

OF ARITHMETIC

Multiplication is vexation,
 Division is as bad;
The rule of Three doth puzzle me,
 And Practice drives me mad.

Bow, wow, wow, Whose dog art thou?
Little Tom Tinker's dog, Bow, bow, wow.

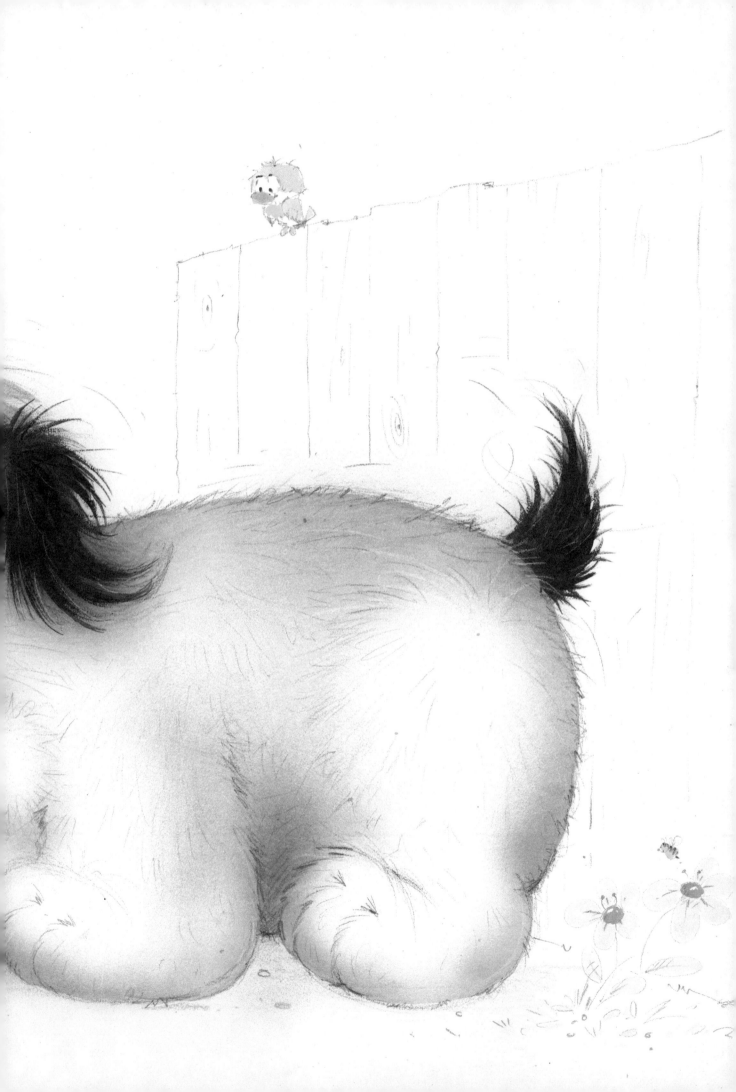

Charley Parley stole the barley
Out of the baker's shop.
The baker came out,
          and gave him a clout,
Which made poor Charley hop.

BOBBY SNOOKS

Little Bobby Snooks was fond of his books,
And loved by his usher and master;

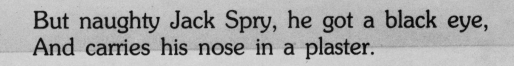

But naughty Jack Spry, he got a black eye,
And carries his nose in a plaster.

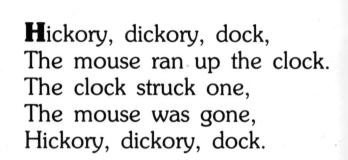

Hickory, dickory, dock,
The mouse ran up the clock.
The clock struck one,
The mouse was gone,
Hickory, dickory, dock.

Rain, rain, go away,
Come again another day.

Twinkle, twinkle, little star, how I wonder what you are,
Up above the world so high, like a diamond in the sky.

In the dark blue sky you keep, Often through my curtains peep,
For you never shut your eye, till the sun is in the sky.

When the blazing sun is gone, when he nothing shines upon,
Then you show your little light, twinkle, twinkle, all the night.

Then the traveller in the dark, thanks you for your tiny spark;
How could he see where to go, if you did not twinkle so.

The Queen of Hearts
She made some tarts,
All on a summer's day;
The Knave of Hearts
He stole the tarts,
And took them right away.

The King of Hearts,
Called for the tarts,
And beat the Knave full sore;
The Knave of Hearts
Brought back the tarts,
And vowed he'd steal no more.

Snail, snail
     put out your horns,
And I'll give you bread
     and barley corns.

My mother said I never should
Play with gypsies in the wood.
If I did, she would say:
'Naughty little girl to disobey.'

There was a crooked man,
    and he walked a crooked mile,
He found a crooked sixpence
    against a crooked stile;
He bought a crooked cat,
    which caught a crooked mouse,
And they all lived together
    in a little crooked house.

Boys and girls come out to play,
The moon doth shine as bright as day.
Leave your supper and leave your sleep,
And join your playfellows in the street.
Come with a whoop and come with a call,
Come with a good will or not at all.
Up the ladder and down the wall,
A half-penny loaf will serve us all;
You find milk, and I'll find flour,
And we'll have a pudding in half an hour.

Peter, Peter, pumpkin eater,
Had a wife and couldn't keep her;
He put her in a pumpkin shell
And there he kept her very well.

MOTHER GOOSE

Old Mother Goose, when
  She wanted to wander,
Would ride through the air
  On a very fine gander.

How do you like to go up in a swing,
Up in the air so blue!
Oh, I do think it the pleasantest thing
Ever a child can do!

Up in the air and over the wall,
Till I can see so wide,
Rivers and trees and cattle and all
Over the countryside –

Till I look down on the garden green,
Down on the roof so brown –
Up in the air I go flying again,
Up in the air and down!

THE LAND OF THE COUNTERPANE

When I was sick and lay a-bed, I had two pillows at my head,
And all my toys beside me lay to keep me happy all the day.

And sometimes for an hour or so I watched my leaden soldiers go,
  With different uniforms and drills, among the bed-clothes, through the hills;

And sometimes sent my ships in fleets all up and down among the sheets;
Or brought my trees and houses out, and planted cities all about.

I was the giant great and still that sits upon the pillow-hill,
And sees before him, dale and plain, the pleasant land of counterpane.

What are little boys made of?
What are little boys made of?
Snaps and snails, and puppy dogs' tails
That's what little boys are made of.

What are little girls made of?
What are little girls made of?
Sugar and spice, and all things nice
That's what little girls are made of.

THE LITTLE HUSBAND

I had a little husband,
  No bigger than my thumb;
I put him in a pint pot,
  And then I bade him drum.

I bought a little horse,
  That galloped up and down;
I bridled him, and saddled him,
  And sent him out of town.

I gave him a pair of garters
  To tie up his little hose,
And a little silk handkerchief
  To wipe his little nose.

Ring a ring o' roses,
A pocket full of posies.
A-tishoo! A-tishoo!
We all fall down.

Jack and Jill went up the hill
To fetch a pail of water,
Jack fell down and broke his crown,
And Jill came tumbling after.

FORTUNE-TELLING BY DAISY PETALS

He loves me, he don't!
He'll have me, he won't!

He would if he could,
But he can't, so he don't!

CAT AND DOG

Pussy sits beside the fire, how can she be fair?
In comes the little dog, "Pussy, are you there?

So, so, Mistress Pussy, pray, how do you do?"
"Thank you, thank you, little dog,
I'm very well just now."

There was a man, and he had nought,
    And robbers came to rob him;
He crept up to the chimney pot,
    And then they thought they had him.

But he got down on t' other side,
    And then they could not find him;
He ran fourteen miles in fifteen days,
    And never looked behind him.

Fee, fi, fo, fum,
I smell the blood of an Englishman:
Be he alive or be he dead,
I'll grind his bones to make my bread.

THE LITTLE CLOCK

There's a neat little clock,
In the schoolroom it stands,
And when it points to the time
With its two little hands.

And may we, like the clock,
Keep a face clean and bright,
With hands ever ready
To do what is right.

Handy-pandy, Jack-a-dandy,
Loved plum cake and sugar-candy;
He bought some at a grocer's shop,
And out he came, hop, hop, hop.

This old man, he played one,
He played Nick Nack
On my drum!
Nick Nack Paddy Wack!
Give a dog a bone,
This old man came rolling home.

Please to remember
The fifth of November,
Gunpowder, treason and plot;
I see no reason
Why gunpowder treason
Should ever be forgot.

Little Tommy Tittlemouse
Lived in a little house.
He caught fishes
In other men's ditches.

There was an old woman
Lived under a hill,
And if she's not gone
She lives there still.

I'M THE KING OF THE CASTLE

I'm the King of the Castle
Get down you dirty rascal.

Ride a cock-horse to Banbury Cross,
To see a fine lady upon a white horse;
Rings on her fingers and bells on her toes,
She shall have music wherever she goes.

Baa, baa, black sheep,
Have you any wool?
Yes, sir, yes, sir,
Three bags full;
One for the master,
And one for the dame,
And one for the little boy
Who lives down the lane.

RIDE AWAY, RIDE AWAY

Ride away, ride away,
  Johnny shall ride,
And he shall have pussy-cat
  tied to one side;
And he shall have little dog
  tied to the other;
And Johnny shall ride
  to see his grandmother.

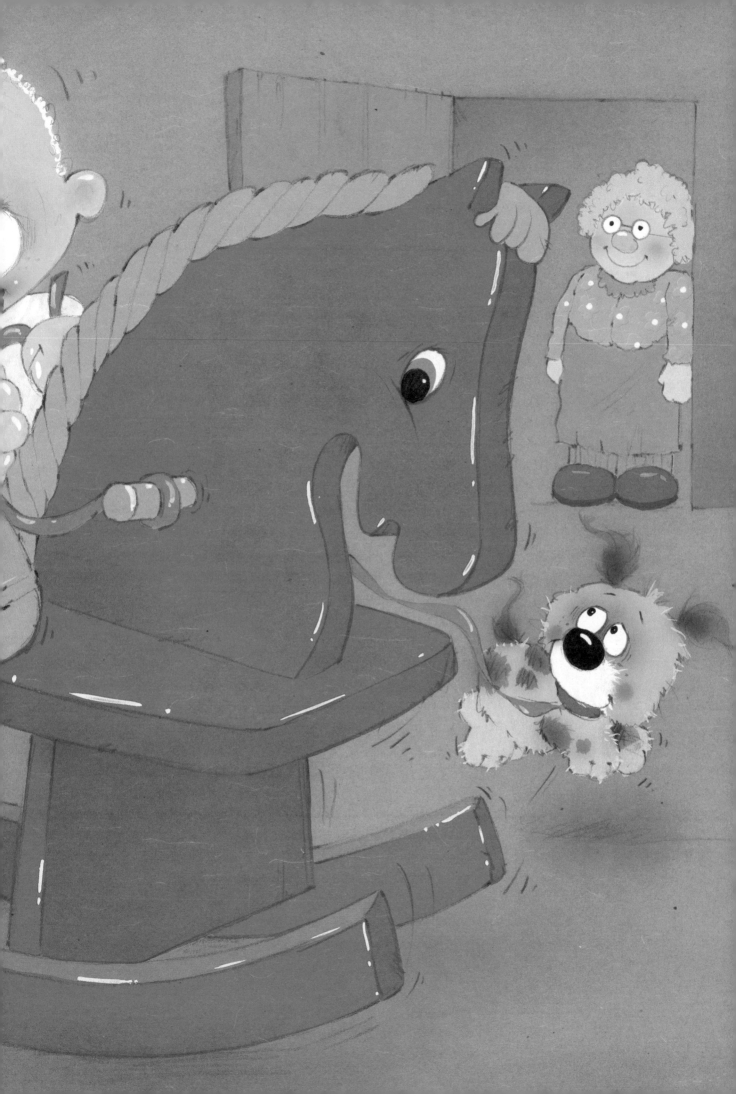

See-saw, Margery Daw,
Johnny shall have a new master;
He shall have but a penny a day,
Because he can't work any faster.

Jack be nimble,
Jack be quick,
Jack jump over
The candlestick.

Where do all the snowmen go?
Tell me please, I want to know.
Where do all the snowmen go?
Disappear dear, with the snow.

Cocks crow in the morn
  To tell us to rise,
And he who lies late
  Will never be wise;

For early to bed
  And early to rise,
Is the way to be healthy
  And wealthy and wise.

Hey diddle diddle,
The cat and the fiddle,
The cow jumped over the moon;
The little dog laughed
To see such fun,
And the dish ran away
        with the spoon.

Simple Simon met a pieman,
Going to the fair,
Says Simple Simon to the pieman,
Let me taste your ware.

Says the pieman to Simple Simon,
Show me first your penny;
Says Simple Simon to the pieman,
Indeed I have not any.

Simple Simon went a-fishing,
For to catch a whale;
All the water he had got
Was in his mother's pale.

Simple Simon went to look
If plums grew on a thistle,
He pricked his finger very much;
Which made poor Simon whistle.

Little Boy Blue,
Come blow your horn,
The sheep's in the meadow,
The cow's in the corn.
But where is the boy
Who looks after the sheep?
He's under a haycock,
Fast asleep.
Will you wake him?
No, not I,
For if I do,
He's sure to cry.

Little Jack Horner sat in a corner,
Eating his Christmas pie;
He put in his thumb,
And pulled out a plum,
And said, "What a good boy am I!"

Go to bed late,
Stay very small;
Go to bed early,
Grow very tall.

Goosey, goosey gander,
Where shall I wander?
Upstairs and downstairs
And in my lady's chamber.

There I met an old man
Who would not say his prayers,
I took him by the left leg
And threw him down the stairs.

The owl and the Pussy-cat went to sea
In a beautiful pea-green boat;
They took some honey, and plenty of money,
Wrapped up in a five-pound note.
The Owl looked up to the stars above,
And sang to a small guitar,
'O lovely Pussy! O Pussy, my love,
What a beautiful pussy you are,
        You are,
        You are!
What a beautiful Pussy you are!'

A SWARM OF BEES

A swarm of bees in May
Is worth a load of hay;
A swarm of bees in June
Is worth a silver spoon;
A swarm of bees in July
Is not worth a fly.

THE LATEST NEWS

What is the news of the day,
Good neighbour, I pray?

They say the balloon
Is gone up to the moon!

Three blind mice, see how they run!
They all ran after the farmer's wife;
She cut off their tails with a carving knife,
Did you ever see such a thing in your life,
As three blind mice?

Little Miss Muffet
Sat on a tuffet,
Eating her curds and whey;
There came a big spider,
Who sat down beside her
And frightened Miss Muffet away.

THE LITTLE MOUSE

I have seen you, little mouse,
Running all about the house,
Through the hole, your little eye
In the wainscot peeping sly,
Hoping soon some crumbs to steal,
To make quite a hearty meal.
Look before you venture out,
See if pussy is about,
If she's gone, you'll quickly run
To the larder for some fun,
Round about the dishes creep,
Taking into each a peep,
To choose the daintiest that's there,
Spoiling things you do not care.

The Land of Nod

From breakfast on through all the day
At home among my friends I stay,
But every night I go abroad
Afar into the land of Nod.

All by myself I have to go,
With none to tell me what to do –
All alone beside the streams
And up the mountainsides of dreams.

The strangest things are there for me,
Both things to eat and things to see,
And many frightening sights abroad
Till morning in the land of Nod.

Try as I like to find the way,
I never can get back by day,
Nor can remember plain and clear
The curious music that I hear.

Polly put the kettle on,
Polly put the kettle on,
Polly put the kettle on,
We'll all have some tea.

Sukey take if off again,
Sukey take if off again,
Sukey take if off again,
They've all gone away.

This little pig went to market,
This little pig stayed at home,
This little pig had roast beef,
This little pig had none,
And this little pig cried "Wee-wee-wee,"
 all the way home.

BLOCK CITY

What are you able to build with your blocks?
Castles and palaces, temples and docks.
Rain may keep raining, and others go roam,
But I can be happy just building at home.

Mary had a little lamb, its fleece was white as snow;
And everywhere that Mary went the lamb was sure to go.

It followed her to school one day, that was against the rule;
It made the children laugh and play to see a lamb at school.

When little Sammy Soapsuds went out to take a ride,
In looking over London Bridge, he fell into the tide.

His parents never having taught their loving Sam to swim,
The tide soon got the mastery, and made an end of him.

Old Mistress McShuttle
Lived in a coal scuttle,
Along with her dog and her cat.
What she ate I can't tell,
But 'tis known very well,
That none of the party was fat.

Rock-a-bye baby, thy cradle is green,
Father's a nobleman, Mother's a queen.
Johnny's a drummer, and drums for the king.
And Betty's a lady, and wears a gold ring.

One, two, buckle my shoe;
Three, four, knock at the door;

Five, six, pick up sticks;
Seven, eight, lay them straight;
Nine, ten, a big fat hen.

ROBIN AND RICHARD

Robin and Richard were two little men,
They did not awake till the clock struck ten;
Then up starts Robin, and looks at the sky;
Oh! brother Richard, the sun's very high!
They both were ashamed, on such a fine day,
When they were wanted to make the new hay.
Do you go before, with bottle and bag,
I will come after on little Jack nag.

The north wind doth blow,
And we shall have snow,
And what will poor robin do then?
Poor thing!

He'll sit in a barn,
And keep himself warm,
And hide his head under his wing.
Poor thing!

A cat came fiddling out of a barn,
With a pair of bagpipes under her arm;
She could sing nothing but fiddle-cum-fee,
The mouse has married the bumblebee.
Pipe, cat; dance, mouse,
We'll have a wedding at our good house.

Little Bo-Peep has lost her sheep,
And doesn't know where to find them;
Leave them alone and they'll come home,
Wagging their tails behind them.

There was a little man,
Who wooed a little maid;
And he said: "Little maid, will you wed, wed, wed?
I have little more to say,
so will you ay or nay
For the least said is soonest mend-ed. ded. ded."

Then the little maid replied:
"Should I be your little bride,
Pray what must we have for to eat, eat, eat?
Will the flame that you're so rich in
Light a fire in the kitchen?
Or the little god of Love turn the spit, spit, spit?"

NOTHING-AT-ALL

There was an old woman
    called Nothing-at-all,
Who rejoiced in a dwelling
    exceedingly small;
A man stretched his mouth
    to its utmost extent,
And down at one gulp
    house and old woman went.

If all the world were paper,
And all the sea were ink,
And all the trees were bread and cheese,
What should we have to drink?

Diddle, diddle, dumpling, my son John,
Went to bed with his trousers on;
One shoe off, and one shoe on,
Diddle, diddle, dumpling, my son John.

Two little dicky birds
Sat upon a wall;
One named Peter
The other named Paul,
Fly away, Peter!
Fly away, Paul!
Come back, Peter!
Come back, Paul!

Doctor Foster went to Gloucester
In a shower of rain;
He stepped in a puddle,
Right up to his middle,
And never went there again.

THE BOY AND THE OWL

There was a little boy who went into a field,
And lay down on some hay;

An owl came out and flew about,
And the little boy ran away.

Humpty Dumpty sat on a wall,
Humpty Dumpty had a great fall,
All the king's horses,
And all the king's men,
Couldn't put Humpty together again.

Pat-a-cake, pat-a-cake,
baker's man,
Bake me a cake,
as fast as you can;
Pat it and prick it
and mark it with B,
And put it in the oven
for baby and me.

St Swithin's day, if thou dost rain,
For forty days it will remain;
St Swithin's day, if thou be fair,
For forty days 'twill rain no more.

This is the house that
Jack built.

This is the malt,
That lay in the house that Jack built.

This is the rat,
That ate the malt,
That lay in the house that Jack built.

This is the cat that killed the rat,
That ate the malt,
That lay in the house that Jack built.

This is the dog
That worried the cat,
That killed the rat,
That ate the malt,
That lay in the house that Jack built.

SIMON BRODIE'S COW

Simon Brodie had a cow;
He lost his cow and could not find her;
When he had done what man could do,
The cow came home and her tail behind her.

Old King Cole
Was a merry old soul,
And a merry old soul was he;
He called for his pipe,
And he called for his bowl,
And he called for his fiddlers three.

Old Mother Hubbard
Went to the cupboard,
To get her poor dog a bone;
But when she got there
The cupboard was bare
And so the poor dog had none.

Pussycat mole jumped over a coal
And in her best petticoat burnt a great hole.
Poor pussy's weeping, she'll have no more milk
Until her best petticoat's mended with silk.

Three little kittens they washed their mittens
And hung them up to dry;
"Oh! Mother dear, look here, look here,
Our mittens we have washed!"
"What washed your mittens, you darling kittens,
But I smell a rat close by!"
Hush! hush! – miaow, miaow,
Miaow, miaow, miaow, miaow.

Ladybird, ladybird, fly away home,
Your house is on fire, and your children all gone;
All but one, and her name is Ann,
And she crept under the frying pan.

Rain on the green grass,
And rain on the tree,
Rain on the house-top,
But not on me.

Rub-a-dub-dub, three men in a tub,
And how do you think they got there?
The butcher, the baker, the candlestick-maker,
They all jumped out of a rotten potato,
'Twas enough to make a man stare.